All Of

Written by Tia Palmer

Illustrated by Isabella Millet

Published by Parker & Co. Press, LLC
P.O. Box 50040
Richmond, VA 23250

ISBN: (paperback): 978-1-952733-22-2
ISBN: (hardback): 978-1-952733-21-5
ISBN: (ebook): 978-1-952733-23-9

DEDICATION

I dedicate this book to grandmothers all over the world, to my grandmas Kitten, Joyce, and Dessie, to Duron, Donte, Taylor, Runoko, and Idris Jr. the people whose little fingers and toes were my inspiration and my bonus daughter Aalaysia.

These are my fingers. These are my toes.

1

How many fingers and toes do you have? Can you count them?

This is a flower. I smell with my nose.

What are some things you can smell with your nose?

4

Can you show me your hands?

These are my feet.

Can you show me your feet?

8

This is my mouth. I use it to speak.

Can you point to your mouth?

10

Cotton candy hair in braids, afro, or a bun.

How do you wear your hair?

Chocolate skin kissed
by the sun.

What fun things do you like to do in the sun?

These are my arms.

Can you wiggle your arms?

These are my legs.

Can you wiggle your legs?

18

Two ears to hear, on both sides of my head.

These are my eyes. I use them to see.

What things can you see?

This is my grandma. She hugs all of me.

Wrap your arms around yourself and give yourself a big hug!

TIA PALMER

is the best-selling author of Career Day. She received a Master's in Teaching from Virginia Commonwealth University and a Doctor of Education degree in Educational Administration & Supervision from Virginia State University. She is an educator who currently resides with her husband and children in Virginia.

CPSIA information can be obtained
at www.ICGtesting.com
Printed in the USA
BVHW091819220321
603180BV00011B/1432